Digging into
LOGIC

by Beverly Post and Sandra Eads

Fearon Teacher Aids
a division of
David S. Lake Publishers
Belmont, California

Designer: Irene Imfeld
Illustrator: Barry Geller

Entire contents copyright © 1987 by David S. Lake Publishers,
500 Harbor Boulevard, Belmont, California 94002. Permission is
hereby granted to reproduce the materials in this book for
noncommercial classroom use.

ISBN 0–8224–4458–5
Printed in the United States of America
1. 9 8 7 6 5 4 3

Contents

Introduction

In today's society, a person must be able to think clearly, analyze information, and reason logically. The notion that these skills cannot be taught is wrong—critical thinking skills *can* be taught and taught to children at a young age.

The matrix problems in *Digging into Logic* were designed to develop critical thinking skills and to give practice in reading, following directions, and writing. While the activities are called logic *problems*, they are more like puzzles, but with one important difference—there are no tricks. Like good puzzles, these logic problems are entertaining and mind stretching. While your students are enjoying themselves, they will also be working toward a very important goal—developing the ability to think, organize, analyze, and arrive at logical conclusions.

How to use this book

The thirty problems in this book have been developed for students in grades five and up. The problems are arranged by difficulty—simple to complex—and can be used either sequentially or individually. You might use the earlier problems to encourage beginners and use the later problems to challenge your gifted students or students who particularly enjoy logic problems.

In the classroom, the logic problems can be used in any one of three ways: (1) as independent activities at learning centers; (2) as extra or supplementary work for students who finish their assigned work early; or (3) as a minicourse in thinking skills for the entire class.

We recommend that you introduce the material by leading the students through the sample problem on pages 2–4. This problem shows how to use a matrix. It also demonstrates some of the logical thinking that is involved in solving a matrix problem. We also suggest that you duplicate and hand out the Matrix Logic Reminder Page on page 5. This sheet details the key points that students should remember when working the problems.

In addition to the problem pages, there are three Make Your Own Logic Problem pages. These pages will help your students design their own logic problems to try on their friends. Constructing logic problems can be as demanding as solving them, so these pages will further build your students' thinking skills.

At the back of the book is an answer key. You should decide whether you want to collect students' completed problems and correct them yourself, duplicate the answers so students can correct their own work, or read the answers aloud to the entire class when all the students are finished. This last alternative allows for further discussion and clarification.

How to Solve Matrix Logic Problems

To solve matrix logic problems, you need to gather information from clues. These clues can be tricky. One clue may give you only a little information by itself, but it may give you a lot of information when you put it together with another clue.

To keep track of all the information in this type of problem, you can use a chart called a *matrix*. (We have included a matrix for each problem in this book.) A matrix will help you keep a logical record of what you learn from each clue, and it will allow you to record the facts that can be deduced by putting together two or more clues. To show you how a matrix works, let's go through a sample problem step-by-step.

Here's the problem:

The Artists

Mark, Meg, Melissa, and Marcie are all artists. One child uses only colored felt pens, one child uses only black pencils, one child uses only watercolors, and one child uses only crayons. Find out what each child uses.

1. Melissa loves bright colors, but she doesn't use felt pens.
2. Marcie and Melissa never have paint on their hands.
3. Mark takes excellent care of his brushes.
4. Meg thinks black pencils are boring.

Here's the matrix:

The first step is to read all the information and then write the names and the categories in the matrix. So in this problem you would write the children's names—Mark, Meg, Melissa, and Marcie—in the boxes on the side, and you would write the four types of art materials—felt pens, pencils, watercolors, and crayons—in the boxes on the top. Here's what your matrix would look like:

	FELT PENS	PENCILS	WATERCOLORS	CRAYONS
MARK				
MEG				
MELISSA				
MARCIE				

Now use the matrix to record the information you get from each of the clues. Let's take the clues in order.

Clue 1: Melissa loves bright colors, but she doesn't use felt pens.

This clue tells you that Melissa doesn't use felt pens, so you would put an **X** (meaning "no") in the box where *Melissa* and *felt pens* meet, like this:

	FELT PENS	PENCILS	WATERCOLORS	CRAYONS
MARK				
MEG				
MELISSA	x			
MARCIE				

You can also deduce from this clue that Melissa does not like to use black pencils, since she loves to use bright colors. Therefore, you would put another **X** where *Melissa* and *pencils* meet. The matrix will look like this:

	FELT PENS	PENCILS	WATERCOLORS	CRAYONS
MARK				
MEG				
MELISSA	×	×		
MARCIE				

Clue 2: Marcie and Melissa never have paint on their hands.

For this clue you would put **X**s where *Melissa* and *watercolors* meet and where *Marcie* and *watercolors* meet. The matrix will look like this:

	FELT PENS	PENCILS	WATERCOLORS	CRAYONS
MARK				
MEG				
MELISSA	×	×	×	
MARCIE			×	

Now study the matrix for a moment. You will notice that all of the art materials in Melissa's row are filled except for crayons. That means that Melissa must use crayons. So now you can put **Yes** in the box where *Melissa* meets *crayons*. Also, since each child uses only one type of material and Melissa uses crayons, the other children can't use crayons. This means you can put **X**s in the rest of the crayon column. At this point the matrix looks like this:

	FELT PENS	PENCILS	WATERCOLORS	CRAYONS
MARK				×
MEG				×
MELISSA	×	×	×	YES
MARCIE			×	×

Clue 3: Mark takes excellent care of his brushes.

This clue tells you that Mark uses watercolors, since they are the only art materials in the list that need brushes. So now you can write **Yes** where *Mark* and *watercolors* meet. You should also put **X**s in the remaining boxes in Mark's row and in the remaining box in the watercolor column. The matrix now looks like this:

	FELT PENS	PENCILS	WATERCOLORS	CRAYONS
MARK	×	×	YES	×
MEG			×	×
MELISSA	×	×	×	YES
MARCIE			×	×

Clue 4: Meg thinks black pencils are boring.

Now you know that Meg doesn't use black pencils, so an **X** goes in that box. This leaves only the *felt pens* box empty in Meg's row, so Meg must use felt pens. The matrix looks like this:

	FELT PENS	PENCILS	WATERCOLORS	CRAYONS
MARK	×	×	YES	×
MEG	YES	×	×	×
MELISSA	×	×	×	YES
MARCIE			×	×

This clue also tells you that Marcie does not use felt pens; therefore an **X** goes where *Marcie* and *felt pens* meet. Once that box is filled in you will notice that there is only one space left—the box where *Marcie* and *pencils* meet. That means you can put **Yes** in that box, and the problem is finished! Here's how the completed matrix looks:

	FELT PENS	PENCILS	WATERCOLORS	CRAYONS
MARK	X	X	YES	X
MEG	YES	X	X	X
MELISSA	X	X	X	YES
MARCIE	X	YES	X	X

You can solve all the matrix problems in *Digging into Logic* using this method. As the problems become more difficult, the matrices will have more boxes. You will find three types of matrices in this book: a simple matrix such as the one we just used in the sample problem, a rectangular matrix, and a complex matrix. A rectangular matrix looks like this:

		Food					Time			
		MEAT LOAF	PEAS	CORN	CHICKEN	SALAD	7:00	8:00	8:05	8:15	9:00
	ALAN										
	BETTY										
Name	CYNTHIA										
	DON										
	ELLIE										

You will usually use this type of matrix if there are more than two categories in the problem. You can complete this matrix the same way you would complete a simple matrix.

There are times when clues don't give you enough information to mark a box **X** or **Yes**. When this happens, make a note next to the appropriate column or row that you can use when you go back over all the clues.

A complex matrix looks like this:

		Food					Time			
		MEAT LOAF	PEAS	CORN	CHICKEN	SALAD	7:00	8:00	8:05	8:15	9:00
	ALAN										
	BETTY										
Name	CYNTHIA										
	DON										
	ELLIE										
	7:00										
	8:00										
Time	8:05										
	8:15										
	9:00										

If you study this matrix for a moment, you will notice that the *time* category is shown twice—once next to the *food* category, and once under the *name* category. This allows you to record clues that relate *time* to *food* as well as *time* to *names*. When you can, always transfer information from one category to another. This type of matrix is used for the hardest problems in the book.

Matrix Logic Reminder Page

1. Read all the information in the problem. Then write the names and the categories in the matrix.
2. Read the clues in order and see what they tell you about each item in the problem and its relationship to other items. If a clue gives you a definite no or yes answer, mark the box with either an **X** (meaning no) or a **Yes.**
3. Whenever you mark a box **Yes,** remember that you can put **X**s in all the other boxes in that row and in all the other boxes in that column.
4. If you find a clue that doesn't give you enough information to mark a definite **X** or **Yes,** make a note next to the box. You can use these notes when you go back over all the clues.
5. Go over each clue again carefully and relate it to other clues. Find two or more clues that fit together to give you enough information to mark a box **Yes** or **X.**
6. When using a complex matrix, remember to transfer information from one category to another. (You don't always have to complete the entire chart.)

1 Rock Around the Block

One Saturday night, three rock groups played in Anytown. The groups were the Remedy, the Rolling Rocks, and the Princess. From the clues given below, find out the order in which the bands played.

1. The Remedy played before the Princess.
2. The Princess played after the Rolling Rocks.
3. The Remedy played after the Rolling Rocks.

2 Bower's Flowers

Mrs. Bower owns the local flower store. It is an unusual store because no two types of flowers have the same color. Mrs. Bower's favorite flowers are the sweet peas, roses, and lilies. Her favorite colors are yellow, purple, and red. What is the color of each type of flower?

1. The roses are kept next to the red flowers.
2. The yellow flowers are not the sweet peas.
3. The sweet peas are in a container next to the purple flowers.
4. The roses are not yellow.

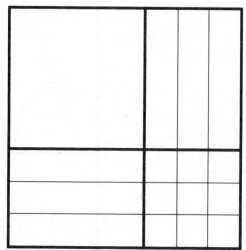

Digging into Logic © 1987 David S. Lake Publishers

3 A Room at the Top

Mr. Height always had wanted an office in the tallest building in the city. Now there were offices available in the three tallest buildings—the Mirror Building, the Tower Building, and the Clock Building. One building is 24 floors high, one is 30 floors high, and one is 40 floors high. Which building did he choose?

1. The Mirror Building is taller than the Clock Building.
2. The tallest building is in the center of town, next to the Tower Building.
3. The Clock Building is taller than the Tower Building.

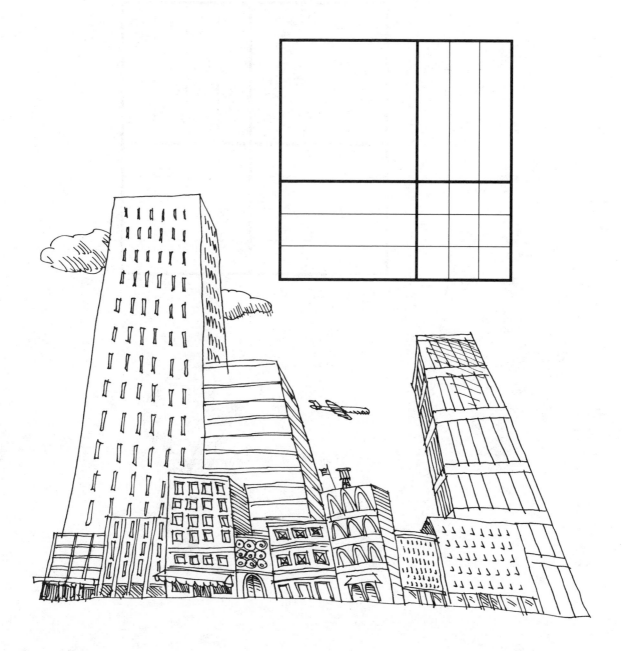

4 Tabby Cat

Sean, Joan, Patty, and George each own a cat. Their cats' names are Tawny Cat, Tiny Cat, Tabby Cat, and Tom Cat. Which person owns Tabby Cat?

1. The first name of Tabby Cat's owner has the letter **a** in it.
2. Tawny Cat's owner is a girl and has an **a** but not an **n** in her first name.
3. The first name of Tiny Cat's owner has an **a** but not an **e**.

Digging into Logic © 1987 David S. Lake Publishers

5 The Picky Pests

Five creatures—a grasshopper, a worm, a snail, a mealybug, and a caterpillar—had a feast in a garden. The garden contained tomatoes, cabbages, daisies, violets, and petunias. Each creature ate only one type of plant. Which creature ate which plant?

1. The caterpillar didn't like tomatoes and liked cabbage even less.
2. The mealybug and the grasshopper liked to eat either daisies, violets, or petunias.
3. The worm liked tomatoes more than the snail did.
4. The grasshopper liked petunias less than violets.
5. The mealybug feasted on violets.

6 Locating Libraries

Billy, Millie, Tillie, and Tom love to read. Each one has a favorite subject, and they get their books from the libraries closest to their homes. The libraries are located on Forty-second Street, Thirty-fourth Street, Tenth Street, and First Street. Find each child's favorite subject and the library to which he or she goes. (Note: the subjects can be found in the clues.)

1. Billy likes to read either histories or biographies.
2. Science fiction is neither Tillie's nor Tom's favorite subject.
3. Tom's library is closest to the First Street Library. He likes histories.
4. Millie does not go to the Forty-second Street Library.
5. The person who reads mysteries goes to the First Street Library.

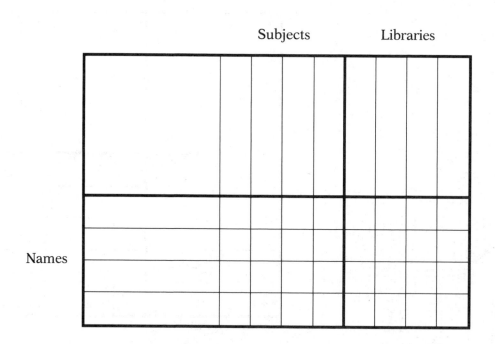

Digging into Logic © 1987 David S. Lake Publishers

7 The Bird Watchers

Mr. Dove, Mrs. Wren, Ms. Tern, Ms. Hawks, and Mr. Pelican are ornithologists (people who study birds). They each have a favorite bird they like to watch. The birds are orioles, robins, sparrows, blue jays, and hummingbirds. Use the information given to find each person's favorite bird.

1. Mr. Dove and the person who watches blue jays are good friends.
2. Either Mrs. Wren or Ms. Tern watches the sparrows.
3. Ms. Hawks likes robins less than orioles—her favorite.
4. Mr. Pelican and Mrs. Wren do not watch the blue jays or the robins.

8 The Scan Clan's Newspaper Plan

The Scan Clan enjoys reading the Sunday newspaper. The Clan members—Papa Scan, Mama Scan, Harriet, Anita, Cedric, and Thomas—each grab a favorite section. The sections they read are the front page, the business section, the travel section, the drama section, the sports page, and the comics. From the clues given below, discover which section each family member reads.

1. Papa Scan likes to relax on Sunday. He doesn't read the front page or the business section.
2. Harriet reads either the drama section or the business section.
3. One of the boys, either Cedric or Thomas, always reads the sports page.
4. Mama Scan always wants to know about current events, which are on the front page.
5. Anita wants to be an actress and reads only the drama section.
6. Thomas likes the travel section best.

Digging into Logic © 1987 David S. Lake Publishers

9 TV Daze

Ben, Carmen, Tod, and Rich each like to watch one type of TV program. The programs are shown at 4:00, 5:00, 7:00, and 9:00 P.M. The types of programs they watch can be found in the clues. Find out the type of program that each person watches and the time it is on.

1. Ben likes to watch soap operas.
2. Carmen doesn't like cartoons, but her friend does.
3. Ben's favorite program comes on later than the programs that Rich and Carmen watch.
4. Rich loves to watch the cartoons that come on right before Carmen's favorite program.
5. The news is on at 5:00, but that is not what Tod watches.
6. The movie is on at 9:00.

	Program				Time			
Name								

Digging into Logic © 1987 David S. Lake Publishers

10 Presenting the Circus DeVille!

The Circus DeVille is in town! Six acts will be featured in the center ring—Tonga the Lion Tamer, the Crazy Clowns, Diz's Trained Dogs, the Tiny Tumblers, the Flying Flynns' Trapeze Act, and the Prancing Horses. The six acts always appear in the same order. Find out what that order is.

1. Tonga comes on immediately after the Flying Flynns.
2. The Tiny Tumblers perform between the Prancing Horses and Diz's Dogs.
3. The Flying Flynns will have to watch four acts before they perform.
4. The Prancing Horses are on before Diz's Dogs but after the Crazy Clowns.
5. The trained dogs come on right before the trapeze act.

Digging into Logic © 1987 David S. Lake Publishers

11 Magico's Magic

Magico the Magician was famous for his disappearing act. One night he made six objects—a hat, a ring, a rabbit, a cat, a wallet, and a watch—vanish. Find out the order, first through sixth, in which the objects disappeared.

1. The watch disappeared immediately after the wallet.
2. The cat vanished after the ring but before the hat.
3. The cat was the third item that disappeared.
4. Magico made four things vanish before he got to the wallet.
5. The ring disappeared after the rabbit.

12 Penguins at the Pole

After a hard day of fishing, seven penguins decided to race to the South Pole. We will call the penguins A, B, C, D, E, F, and G. Which penguin won the race, and in what order did the others arrive?

1. F arrived before three of the penguins and after three others.
2. B came in after the penguin who arrived fourth but before A and C.
3. C was very happy not to be last.
4. E did not win but arrived before D.

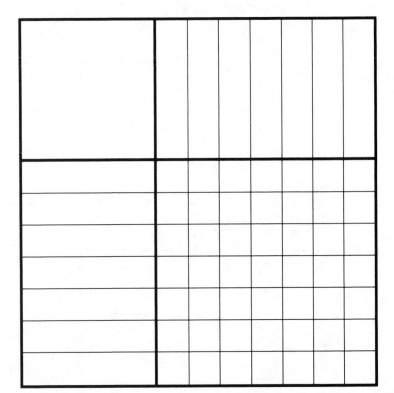

Digging into Logic © 1987 David S. Lake Publishers

13 Saturday's Supper

Saturday night was the tennis club's annual potluck dinner party. Alice, Sandra, Mike, Tony, Don, Barbara, and Kate all signed up to bring food. The types of food they brought can be found in the clues. Who brought what?

1. Alice and Sandra did not bring the pie or the potato salad.
2. Mike and Tony didn't bring the chicken, but Don did.
3. Barbara and Kate each brought something. One of them made a casserole and the other brought fruit.
4. Either Mike or Kate brought the pie. The other brought the casserole.
5. One of the women brought nuts, but it wasn't Alice.
6. Someone brought punch.

14 Active Athletes

Milo, Max, Mary, Marvin, and Maria all take weekly lessons in their favorite sports. These sports are karate, tennis, swimming, gymnastics, and golf. Their lessons are on weekdays only. In what sport and on what day does each person take his or her lesson?

1. Maria's lesson is on Monday.
2. Marvin's coach doesn't teach on Tuesdays and Thursdays.
3. Max takes a lesson on Thursday, the day after Marvin's lesson.
4. The gymnastics coach works only on Mondays.
5. The karate coach teaches on Wednesdays.
6. Mary doesn't have a lesson on Friday.
7. The tennis coach teaches the day after Marvin's lesson.
8. Milo likes swimming more than any other sport.

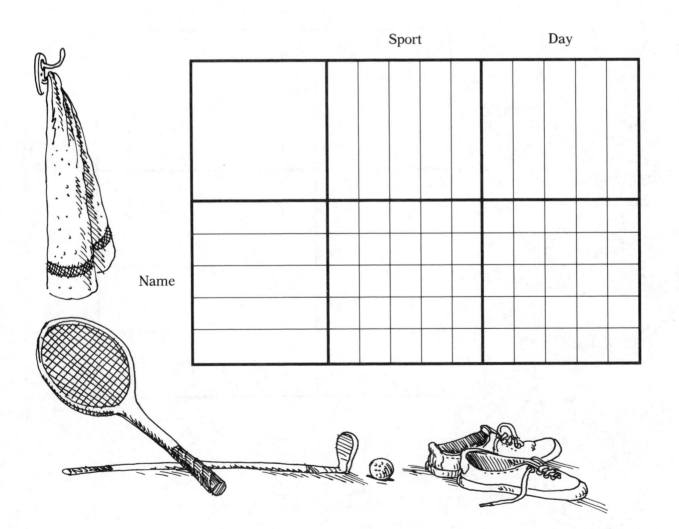

Sport   Day

Name

Digging into Logic © 1987 David S. Lake Publishers

15 Helpful Heroes

Flyman, Superbat, Mighty Mite, Cat Girl, Wonder Mouse, and Tiger Lady each performed an incredible rescue. They each saved someone from one of the following predicaments: a burning building, bandits, a sinking ship, a cattle stampede, a runaway stagecoach, and a mountain lion. The people in trouble were Cowboy Boris, Zelda Zill, Cromwell West, Mary Beth, Angela Star, and Indian Joe. Whom did each hero rescue and from what?

1. While Cat Girl was rescuing Zelda Zill, Indian Joe was captured by bandits.
2. Superbat saved the person whose last name rhymes with "tar" from the burning building.
3. None of the rescued men were near the sinking ship, but two were saved from the cattle stampede and the mountain lion.
4. Wonder Mouse rescued Mary Beth while Flyman captured the bandits.
5. Cromwell West was not saved by Tiger Lady, who was busy at the stampede.
6. Wonder Mouse stopped the runaway stagecoach.

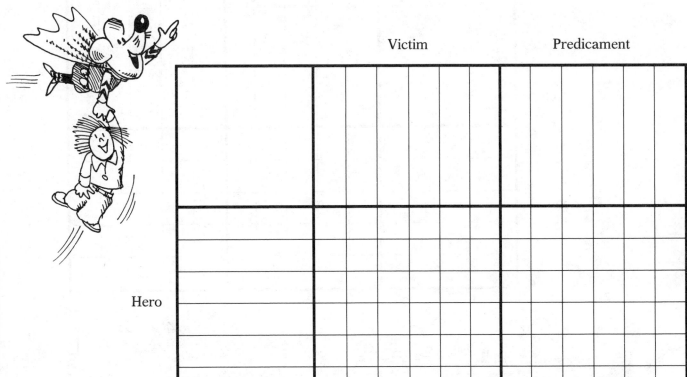

Digging into Logic © 1987 David S. Lake Publishers

16 Ships at Sea

Five ships—the *Mary Star*, the *Royal Princess*, the S.S. *North*, the *Whitehead*, and the *Haku Maru*—all set sail for a different international port. The ports are Los Angeles, Bergen, Cairo, Sydney, and Vancouver. At which port did each ship arrive, and which ship was the first to reach its destination?

1. The *Haku Maru* did not dock in Sydney or Cairo, and it was not the first to arrive.
2. The *Mary Star* was not the first or last to dock, but it arrived before the *Royal Princess*.
3. The third ship to arrive docked in Los Angeles, and the second ship to arrive docked in Sydney. Both docked after the S.S. *North*, which went to Cairo.
4. The *Whitehead* was the second ship to reach its destination.
5. Bergen is where the ship that arrived before the *Haku Maru* docked.

Port   Order

Name

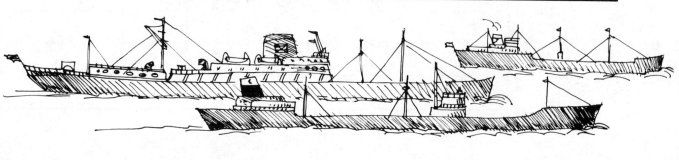

Digging into Logic © 1987 David S. Lake Publishers

17 Creepy Creatures

In an old haunted house lived five creatures—a goblin, a witch, a ghost, a black cat, and a bat. They made funny noises. One creature screamed, one hummed, one screeched, one whistled, and one giggled. Each creature lived in a special place—the attic, the chimney, the first floor, the second floor, or the basement. Put the clues together to find out about each creature.

1. The goblin loved living in the chimney but did not enjoy listening to the creatures who giggled and whistled.
2. The ghost thought her scream was beautiful.
3. The cat lived on the floor right below the attic, and the bat lived on the first floor.
4. The creature who lived in the attic loved to hear herself hum to the bat and the goblin.
5. The creature who lived in the basement did not get along with the bat or the creature who whistled.
6. The creature who screamed lived at the very bottom of the house.

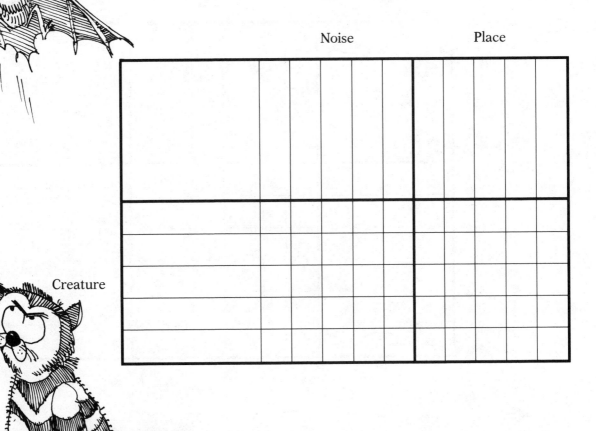

18 Play Ball

Three men—Butch, Riley, and Moose—and three women—Iris, Vicki, and Tiny—play on a recreational softball team. Their positions are catcher, pitcher, first base, second base, third base, and shortstop. Find out each player's position and the order in which they come up to bat—first, second, third, and so on.

1. The three women practice together. They are Vicki, the catcher, and the shortstop. None of them bat in the third, fourth, or fifth positions.
2. Riley is the pitcher, and he is married to the woman who plays third base.
3. Tiny bats first, but she is not the catcher.
4. Butch and the two men who bat fourth and fifth are old friends.
5. The person who plays second base bats fifth.
6. Iris doesn't bat second.

	Position						Order to bat					
Name												

Digging into Logic © 1987 David S. Lake Publishers

19 Movie Mania

Five local theaters—the Cinerama, the Odyssey, the Century, the Star, and the Bijou—show comedies, science fiction films, musicals, old movies, and new movies on different nights of the week. Each of five people has a favorite type of movie and goes to a different theater on a different night. The nights are Sunday, Tuesday, Wednesday, Friday, and Saturday. Find the theater, the type of movie, and the night that each person attends. The people's names can be found in the clues.

1. Ken loves comedies, but he does not go to a show on Saturday or Sunday. He has never been to the Bijou.
2. Sue goes only to the theater that shows old movies, which is not the Star or the Century.
3. Adam and Teri are allowed to go to the movies on Tuesdays or Wednesdays because the shows start at 6:00 P.M.
4. Teri does not go to musicals or to the Century.
5. Dameon goes to the movies on Sundays. He does not like to see musicals.
6. The Century features science fiction movies.
7. Musicals are shown at the Odyssey on Tuesday nights.
8. The Bijou never has old movies.

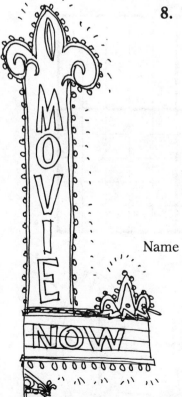

	Theater					Type of movie					Day				
Name															

20 Rise and Shine

Five children live in the same apartment building. Each child gets up at a certain time, either 6:00, 7:00, 7:45, 8:00, or 8:30 A.M. Amber, Craig, Jill, Stacey, and Gil live in apartments lettered A, B, C, D, and E. Find out what time each child gets up, his or her apartment letter, and his or her age. Their ages are nine, ten, twelve, fourteen, and fifteen.

1. Craig gets up at 6:00 to catch the school bus. He is older than the person in Apartment B.
2. Amber, who is twelve, gets up exactly two hours later than the boy who lives in Apartment A.
3. The youngest child, a girl, doesn't live in Apartment E.
4. The girl who is ten lives in Apartment B. It isn't Stacey.
5. The person who lives in Apartment B gets up later than anyone else in the apartment building.
6. Gil is younger than Craig and lives in Apartment D.
7. The shades go up at 7:45 in Apartment C.

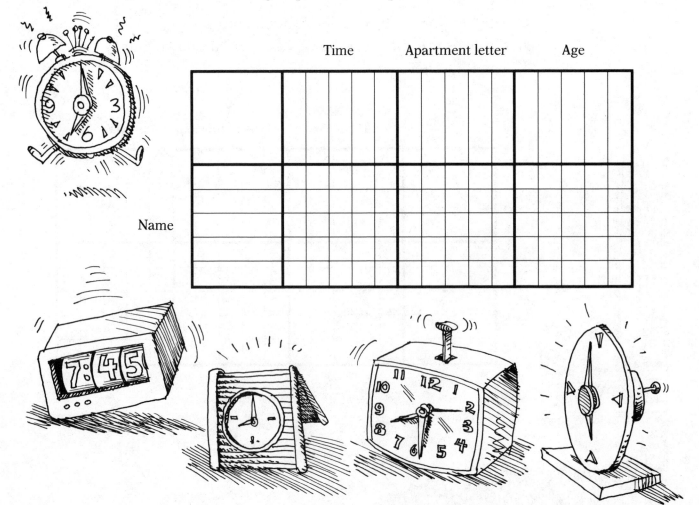

Name

Time Apartment letter Age

Digging into Logic © 1987 David S. Lake Publishers

21 Start Your Engines

The Grand Prix Auto Race is held once a year. This year four drivers—
J. Jones, S. Smith, T. Thomas, and A. Adams—entered the race. They
finished in first, second, third, and fourth places. From the clues, find
out each driver's nickname, car color, and position in the race.

1. Jones's nickname is not Flash, and he drove either a blue or a
   green car.
2. Jones came in third, which was ahead of Thomas.
3. There was a red car in the race.
4. Peppy was right behind Smith, who was driving a blue car.
5. The yellow car was driven by Sprint and did not finish in first place.
6. Adams's car was ahead of Speed's blue car all the way.

	Nickname				Car color				Position			
Name												

22 How Does the Band Stand?

John, Nancy, Rita, and Art play in their school's marching band. Each of the students plays a different instrument—trumpet, tuba, flute, or clarinet. The students all march in different rows. One is in row 1, another is in row 5, the third is in row 8, and the fourth is in row 12. What instrument does each person play and in which row does he or she march? (Note: you may have to read through all of the clues several times!)

1. Art is in a row behind Rita.
2. The person who plays trumpet is in a row behind Nancy.
3. John is not in a row ahead of Art.
4. Rita's row is ahead of the trumpet player's.
5. The tuba player is in the last row.
6. Nancy is not in the fifth row.
7. The person in the first row plays the flute.

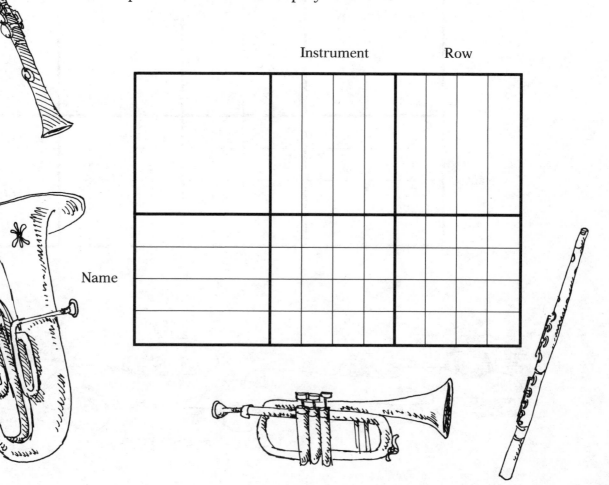

Digging into Logic © 1987 David S. Lake Publishers

23 Astro Robots

The Astro Candy Company uses five robots in its factory. Radar, Tobor, Zotto, Marvel, and Squeaky fill the jobs of order taker, candy dipper, inspector, candy wrapper, and shipper. Each robot works in a different department. These departments are called alpha, beta, delta, gamma, and epsilon. Match each robot with its job and department.

1. Squeaky got its name because it squeaks so much when it loads the candy for shipping.
2. Tobor used to work in the wrapping department but was switched to the beta department.
3. Zotto thinks that alpha is the best department and is very happy not to be a candy dipper in the epsilon department.
4. Alpha and beta are not the departments that take orders or do the shipping.
5. Marvel and the robots that work in delta and gamma were all made the same year.
6. The inspector and Radar do not work very hard, but the robots in delta and alpha do.

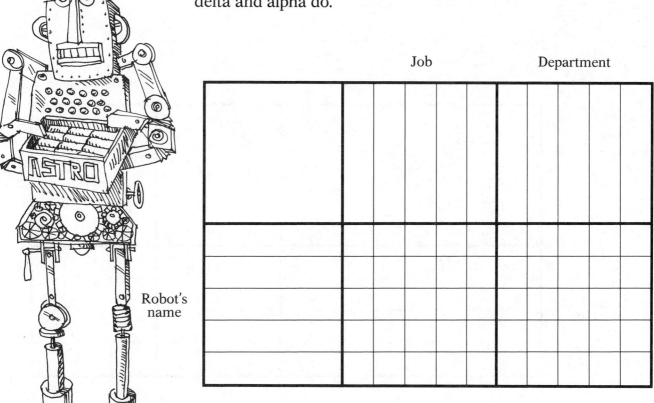

Job   Department

Robot's name

Digging into Logic © 1987 David S. Lake Publishers

29

24 The Computer Club Committee

Phil, Jill, Zill, and Will belong to a school computer club. They formed a committee to design computer programs to help the English, math, social studies, and science teachers. Each student helped one teacher—either Mr. Gill, Ms. Hill, Mr. Pill, or Ms. Dill. The teachers taught in rooms 7, 12, 14, and 19. Match each computer whiz to a teacher, subject, and room number.

1. Will had never met Ms. Hill or Mr. Gill, but he knew the science and English teachers. He helped one of the teachers he knew.
2. Zill did not help the English teacher in Room 14 or the teacher in Room 12.
3. Phil worked with the math teacher in Room 7.
4. Ms. Dill, in Room 14, did not teach science.
5. Mr. Pill did not teach math or social studies.
6. Jill had known Ms. Hill a long time and enjoyed helping her with the computer program.

	Teacher				Subject				Room number			
Student's name												

Digging into Logic © 1987 David S. Lake Publishers

25 Everywhere's Yearly Event

Each year the city of Everywhere has a talent show. Last year the show had six acts—an impersonator, a juggler, a magician, a singer, a mime, and a pianist. The performers were Carl, Sam, Vincent, Norma, Justin, and Sally. Each performer wore a different-colored costume (yellow, purple, red, orange, black, or blue). Find out what color each person wore, his or her talent, and how he or she placed in the contest (first through sixth).

1. Sally and the woman who wore black were friends of the mime.
2. Carl and the man who wore orange had studied music together. One sang; the other played the piano.
3. Norma dropped most of the balls she was juggling and placed next to last in the contest.
4. Vincent, Sally, and the person who wore red were happy they made first, second, and third place.
5. Sam was not the winner, but he did place higher than Justin and Carl.
6. The magician always wore red. That wasn't Justin because he wore orange.
7. The person who wore blue came in last. He did not sing.
8. The impersonator placed higher than the person who wore yellow. However, the person who wore yellow placed higher than the person who wore red.

	Placement						Talent						Costume color					
Name																		

Digging into Logic © 1987 David S. Lake Publishers

26 Inside/Outside

Mike, Allie, Adam, Iris, Bill, and Samantha each enjoy one special indoor activity and one outdoor sport. The indoor activities they enjoy are chess, backgammon, card games, video games, checkers, and reading. You will find the outdoor sports among the clues. What sport and what indoor activity does each person prefer?

1. The person who enjoys playing video games also enjoys horseback riding.
2. Mike and Adam are the people who enjoy skiing and roller-skating, but neither of them knows how to play chess or checkers.
3. The volleyball player does not know Samantha or the checkers player.
4. The person who roller-skates enjoys reading.
5. Iris and Bill need water for their sports, which are surfing and fishing. They do not play cards or chess.
6. Bill and the backgammon player sometimes eat lunch with Adam and the person who plays cards.
7. The person who fishes does not play backgammon.

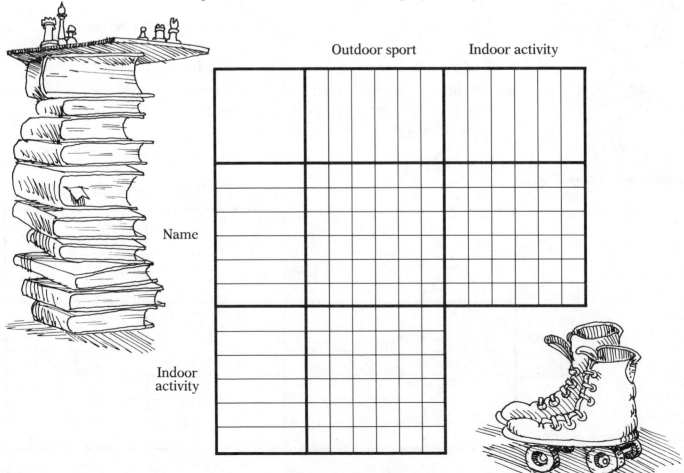

Outdoor sport   Indoor activity

Name

Indoor activity

Digging into Logic © 1987 David S. Lake Publishers

27 Who Does What?

A group of people went to a meeting in San Francisco. The people were originally from Omaha, Detroit, Minneapolis, Los Angeles, and Houston. They each have a different hobby—one collects stamps, one collects coins, one studies the earth, one studies insects, and one studies the origins of words. The correct titles for people who do these things are (in no particular order) philatelist, entomologist, geologist, etymologist, and numismatist. Match the hobby, title, and city of each person.

1. The etymologist lives in Los Angeles, and the entomologist lives in Detroit.
2. The geologist, who likes to study the earth, does not live in Minneapolis or Omaha.
3. The stamp collector has not met the numismatist or the person who lives in Detroit.
4. The person who enjoys studying the origins of words lives in Los Angeles.
5. The person who lives in Detroit has a marvelous insect collection.
6. The philatelist lives in Omaha and is not the person who is interested in coins.

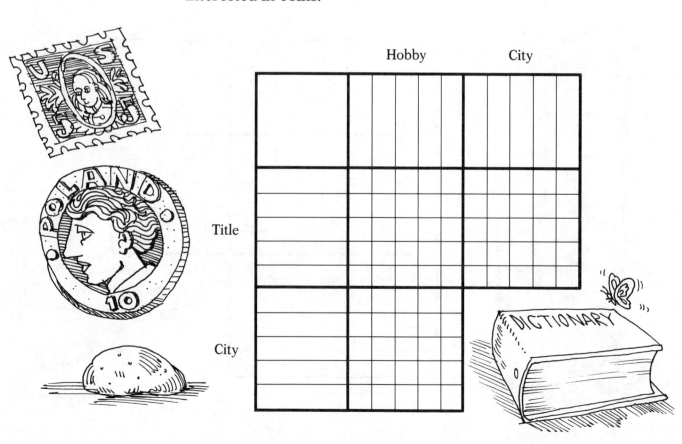

28 Logo Logic

Charles, Philip, Cynthia, Anna, and Margaret each own an important company. All of the companies have very unusual names—MapCo, RatCo, SatCo, TrapCo, and HatCo. Each company has its own logo (symbol for the company). The logos are a hat, a chair, a rat, a map, and a mousetrap. However, none of the logos have anything to do with the company's name. That is your first clue! Now determine the owner and logo of each company.

1. Cynthia uses the rat logo because she loves all kinds of animals.
2. HatCo uses either the mousetrap or the map for its logo.
3. The company Anna owns does not use the map logo.
4. The woman who owns RatCo thought a chair would be a nice logo for her company.
5. Philip uses a mousetrap for his company's logo, just because he likes the look of it.
6. The name of Margaret's company contains the first letters of her first, middle, and last names.
7. The owner of TrapCo does not like Cynthia's logo.

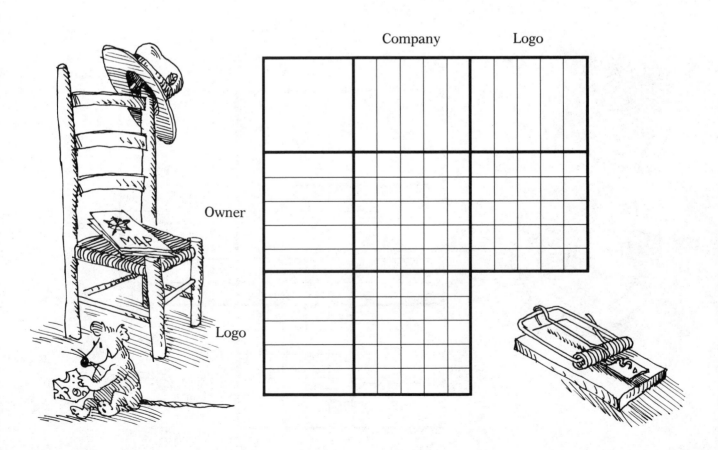

Digging into Logic © 1987 David S. Lake Publishers

29 Student Switch

Tanya, Gerald, Susan, Gina, Joseph, and Alan are exchange students from Japan, Israel, Sweden, Denmark, Germany, and Algeria (in no particular order). Each student also visited one of these countries. Use the clues to find out which country each student came from and which country each student visited.

1. No one went to or came from a country that begins with the first letter of his or her name.
2. Gerald's home country is Algeria. He did not visit Israel.
3. The girls from Germany and Israel had never met the boys who went to Denmark or Algeria, but they did know the boy from Sweden.
4. The person who went to Germany was from Japan.
5. The girl who went to Sweden came from Germany.
6. The person from Israel went to Japan.

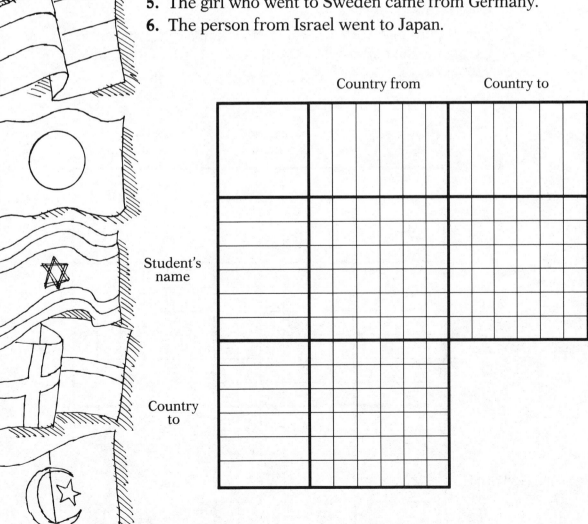

Country from   Country to

Student's name

Country to

30 Chess Challenge

Elise, Jason, Kirk, Bev, Jim, and Carla competed in a big chess tournament. Each of the players invited a special friend to cheer him or her on. Their names were Monica, Tim, Kevin, Kimberly, Wayne, and Theresa. Determine the friend of each player and the prize, first through sixth, that each player won.

1. Jason did not win, although he did place higher than Bev and Jim.
2. The boy who came in third was glad Kimberly rooted for him.
3. Theresa's friend came in last.
4. Monica had hoped to go with Carla to the tournament, but she had already promised to go with another girl.
5. Kevin's girlfriend came in fourth; he really cheered her on!
6. Wayne had come to root for one of the boys, and he was delighted when his friend finished in one of the top two spots. Wayne's friend is not Kirk.
7. Bev did not play too well. She finished in a better position than Carla, but she did not do as well as Monica's friend and Kirk.
8. Tim did not know any of the girl players.
9. Kimberly had never met Jason.

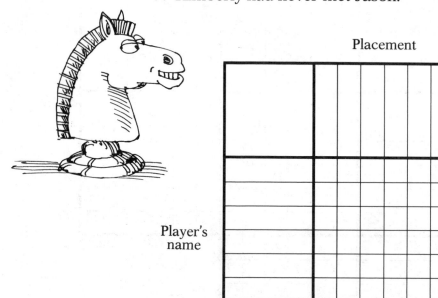

Placement   Friend's name

Player's name

Friend's name

Digging into Logic © 1987 David S. Lake Publishers

Make Your Own Logic Problem

To start you off, try this:

1. Use the following categories: baseball, football, and soccer.
2. Make up the names of three people.
3. Place the names and categories in the matrix below (the names on the left, the categories on the top).

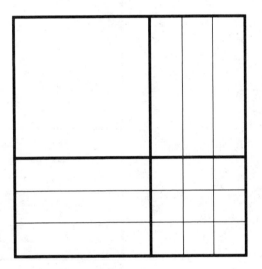

4. Select and fill in your desired answers.
5. Write five clues that will lead to the solution of your problem.

A. _____

B. _____

C. _____

D. _____

E. _____

6. Now give the clues to a friend. Your friend must make a matrix and solve the problem.

Make Your Own Logic Problem

This time, make up a problem using four kinds of food. Choose names for four people.

1. Place the names and the categories you selected in the matrix below.

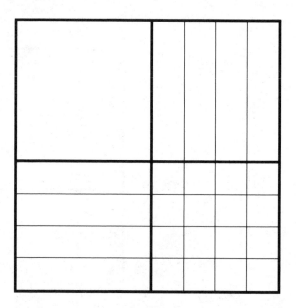

2. Select and fill in your answers to the matrix.
3. Now write clues that will lead to the solution of your problem.

A. _____

B. _____

C. _____

D. _____

E. _____

F. _____

4. Give the clues to a friend. Your friend must make a matrix and solve the problem.

Digging into Logic © 1987 David S. Lake Publishers

Make Your Own Logic Problem

Try creating a problem using two different categories: hair color and age.

1. Select three different hair colors, three different ages, and three children's names.
2. Write the names, ages, and hair colors in the matrix.

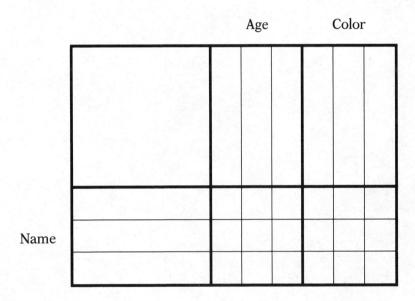

3. Decide on your answers and complete the matrix.
4. Make up clues that will lead to the solution of your problem.

   A. _____

   B. _____

   C. _____

   D. _____

   E. _____

5. Now give the clues to a friend. Your friend must make a matrix and solve the problem.

Answer Key

1. **Rock Around the Block,** page 7
   Remedy—second
   Rolling Rocks—first
   Princess—third

2. **Bower's Flowers,** page 8
   Lilies—yellow
   Sweet peas—red
   Roses—purple

3. **A Room at the Top,** page 9
   Mirror Building—40 floors
   Tower Building—24 floors
   Clock Building—30 floors

4. **Tabby Cat,** page 10
   Sean—Tabby Cat
   Joan—Tiny Cat
   Patty—Tawny Cat
   George—Tom Cat

5. **The Picky Pests,** page 11
   Grasshopper—daisies
   Worm—tomatoes
   Snail—cabbages
   Mealybug—violets
   Caterpillar—petunias

6. **Locating Libraries,** page 12
   Billy—biographies—42nd St.
   Millie—science fiction—34th St.
   Tillie—mysteries—1st St.
   Tom—histories—10th St.

7. **The Bird Watchers,** page 13
   Mr. Dove—robins
   Mrs. Wren—sparrows
   Ms. Tern—blue jays
   Ms. Hawks—orioles
   Mr. Pelican—hummingbirds

8. **The Scan Clan's Newspaper Plan,** page 14
   Papa—comics
   Mama—front page
   Anita—drama
   Harriet—business
   Cedric—sports
   Thomas—travel

9. **TV Daze,** page 15
   Ben—soap operas—7:00
   Carmen—news—5:00
   Tod—movies—9:00
   Rich—cartoons—4:00

10. **Presenting the Circus DeVille!** page 16
    Crazy Clowns—first
    Prancing Horses—second
    Tiny Tumblers—third
    Diz's Dogs—fourth
    Flying Flynns—fifth
    Tonga—sixth

11. **Magico's Magic,** page 17
    rabbit—first
    ring—second
    cat—third
    hat—fourth
    wallet—fifth
    watch—sixth

12. **Penguins at the Pole,** page 18
    G—first
    E—second
    D—third
    F—fourth
    B—fifth
    C—sixth
    A—seventh

13. **Saturday's Supper,** page 19
    Alice—punch
    Sandra—nuts
    Mike—pie
    Tony—potato salad
    Don—chicken
    Kate—casserole
    Barbara—fruit

14. **Active Athletes,** page 20
    Milo—swimming—Friday
    Max—tennis—Thursday
    Mary—golf—Tuesday
    Marvin—karate—Wednesday
    Maria—gymnastics—Monday

15. **Helpful Heroes,** page 21
    Flyman—Indian Joe—bandits
    Superbat—Angela Star—building
    Mighty Mite—Cromwell West—lion
    Cat Girl—Zelda Zill—sinking ship
    Wonder Mouse—Mary Beth—stagecoach
    Tiger Lady—Cowboy Boris—stampede

Digging into Logic © 1987 David S. Lake Publishers